Keeping Pigs

Garden Farming Series

Keeping Pigs

Elisabeth Downing

PELHAM BOOKS/Stephen Greene Press

PELHAM BOOKS/Stephen Greene Press
Published by the Penguin Group
27 Wrights Lane, London W8 5TZ, England
Viking Penguin Inc., 40 West 23rd Street, New York,
New York 10010, USA
Stephen Greene Press Inc, 15 Muzzey Street, Lexington,
Massachusetts 02173, USA
Penguin Books Australia Ltd, Ringwood, Victoria, Australia
Penguin Books Canada Ltd, 2801 John Street, Markham,
Ontario, Canada L3R 1B4
Penguin Books (NZ) Ltd, 182-190 Wairau Road, Auckland 10,
New Zealand

Penguin Books Ltd, Registered Offices: Harmondsworth,
Middlesex, England

First published 1978
Paperback edition 1985
Laminated hard cover edition 1989

Made and printed in Great Britain by Hollen Street Press Ltd., Slough
Filmset by BAS Printers Limited, Over Wallop, Hampshire

British Library Cataloguing in Publication Data

Downing, Elisabeth, 1933—
  Keeping pigs.
  1. Agricultural industries. Smallholdings.
  Livestock; Pigs, Care & management—
  Amateurs' manuals
  I. Title
  636.4'083
  ISBN 0-7207-1846-5

Contents

They [the flitches of bacon] are great softeners of
temper and promotors of domestic harmony.

William Cobbett (1762–1835) *Cottage Economy*

Acknowledgements

I am grateful to J. Crispin Clark, BVMS, MRCVS for valuable suggestions and guidance in the chapter on pig health, although of course all opinions expressed are my responsibility. Thanks are also due to Mr Raymond Sims for advice and to Mr Ken Penney of ECO 2000 for suggestions.

Dulcie Asker has expertly typed the final manuscript for which I am very grateful. I must thank my patient husband who deciphered, corrected and typed the initial copy, annotated the figures, supplied the cover photograph and encouraged me; also John Downing for his valuable practical advice on building pig hotels.

Introduction

How many of us can now afford to indulge regularly in that traditional English breakfast of bacon and eggs? In order to economise we are reduced to buying trimmings from the bacon slicer or the remains of joints commonly known as 'bacon ends'. With luck the best pieces can be carefully trimmed, and these embellished with tomatoes and mushrooms. But too often, the reason that these are described as 'ends' is that they have graced the bacon counter too long, are curling at the edges and may even be inclined to taste rancid.

The very fact that you have been tempted to open this book may well mean that you are tired of going to work on a lonely egg and long for a decently fresh, flavoursome rasher of bacon or two. You may be sick of scouring both town and countryside for a butcher who sells a good joint of firm, pink pork rather than the supermarket's convenience-packed, plastic-covered trays of tasteless, flabby, pale slabs of meat cut from the carcases of factory-reared pigs.

Some may remember the time when those with a pig sty at the bottom of the garden exchanged their wartime weekly bacon ration coupons for pig-meal from the local miller. This, augmented by household and garden scraps, supplied pork and bacon beyond the wildest dreams of the ration-bound town-dweller.

We are *now* regaled by accounts of 'knitted meat' stews and curries enjoyed by the younger generation at school; '. . . you can't even tell the difference . . .' we are sometimes told! Why not show them the unforgettable flavour and delicious aroma of home-grown baked pork?

This book endeavours to help to explain how we *can* grow our own pork, cure our own bacon and indulge in such old-fashioned delicacies as grilled trotters, faggots and scrapple; not to mention a plump and flavoursome leg of pork and firm, tender pork chops which will bear no relation to most of the factory-reared, shop-bought pork.

Our pig is the most economical of beasts to grow, slaughter and butcher, everything being used except for the grunt.

Conversion Table

Metric and Imperial Equivalents

Imperial	Metric	Metric	Imperial
1 inch	2·54 cm	1 cm	0·39 in.
1 foot	30·48 cm	1 cm	0·033 ft
1 yard	0·91 m	1 m	1·094 yds
1 mile	1·61 km	1 km	0·62 miles
1 sq. yd	0·84 sq. m	1 sq. m	1·196 sq. yds
1 cu. yd	0·76 cu. m	1 cu. m	1·31 cu. yds
1 pint	0·57 litre	1 litre	1·76 pints
1 gal	0·0056 cu. m	1 cu. m	219·97 gals
1 gal	4·55 litre	1 litre	0·22 gals
1 fl oz	28·4 ml	1 ml	0·035 fl oz
1 oz	28·35 g	1 g	0·035 oz
1 lb	0·45 kg	1 kg	2·20 lb
1 acre	0·405 hectare	1 hectare	2·47 acres
$x\,°F$	$\frac{5}{9}(x-32)\,°C$	$y\,°C$	$(\frac{9}{5}y+32)\,°F$

Metric abbreviations

cm	centimetre
m	metre
km	kilometre
ml	millilitre
g	gram
kg	kilogram

The Pros and Cons of Pig Keeping

There is no such thing as *the* pig. There are innumerable pigs and they are all different. However, with reasonable care and an adequate diet they can grow into animals which, after slaughter, will yield a rich harvest of joints, chops, sausages and all the delectable delicacies produced from the offal. Alternatively we can subject parts or all of the carcase to a choice of cures and even smoking, which will produce bacon and hams of superb flavour.

It is worth spending some little time considering both the advantages and disadvantages of owning pigs before rushing out to bowl for the pig at the next garden fete.

In the early nineteenth century, William Cobbett advised that the cottager's pig should be bought in the spring at four months and fattened for a year to produce a 200 to 250 kg carcase which would yield more solid and nutritious meat than that of the younger animal. However, nowadays with improved breeds and more enlightened feeding, farmers slaughter porkers at three and a half to four months of age weighing 45 to 50 kg, and pigs destined for the bacon trade at the age of about five to six months and weighing 85 to 90 kg. If a healthy weaner about six weeks old is bought, a minimum of ten weeks will be required to rear him to slaughter-weight, while the larger baconer may require four to five months' fattening. We have found that this relatively short rearing period means that the purchase of weaners can be adjusted to fit in with household arrangements or a possible flush of spring milk from a cow or goat. The pig residence can then be cleaned out and rested for a period.

Household scraps can help to cut down the cost of proprietary pig food, as can spare vegetables from the garden and even food grown especially for them. If a pair of weaners is reared, the sale of one to a friend or neighbour can help to pay for any purchased foodstuffs and *may* even mean that the pig which is kept for home slaughter is fattened cost-free.

Many older homes in country areas will have a pig sty which with renovation and a good spring-clean will house the backyard pig adequately. Failing this, building a sty from concrete blocks can be done relatively cheaply, simply and reasonably swiftly.

The manure which results from keeping a few pigs each year will ensure a fertile vegetable garden, any surplus being given away or sold.

We have found pigs to be generally most intelligent and charming creatures. If they have initially been shy and timid, it has not been long before they have become friendly and affectionate. Of course there is always the exception to the rule like the one we had

Fig. 1 All pigs love to be scratched.

which would insist on leaping out of windows (and it wasn't because he was hungry!), and another which would bite the toes out of wellington boots if given the chance. Some are natural bullies, but a sharp word combined with a timely smack will usually prevent this habit from developing. Remember a charming, cavorting piglet is going to turn into well over 50 kg of fat pig which, if not disciplined, can easily knock over the unwary even if only in fun.

Some pigs we have kept have been able to be let out free on occasions and have followed their feeder around like a dog. In 1803 a certain Mr F. W. Sykes trained a stray sow from the New Forest 'to point and stand at game as staunch as any dog' and named her 'Slut'. In parts of France pigs are still trained to hunt truffles. On the other hand we did have a pair which had no homing instinct at all, and on getting out each would make a beeline in the opposite direction, resisting all but the strongest attempts to catch and pull or drive them back home. Needless to say we kept them no longer than was necessary and killed them at pork-weight. However, whatever their characteristics alive, home-fattened pigs are far superior in flavour to the majority of shop-bought pigs.

The disadvantages of keeping a backyard pig must be carefully considered. While the beast is with you it will need feeding twice daily and an observant eye cast over its general health, attitude and appetite. Its water supply and bedding material must be checked and its dung always noted (this is a good indicator to its health). Now, watching these points may be fun at first, but after the novelty wears off a lack of attention to any one of them *may* result in an ailing pig which for lack of timely professional advice and treatment may die. A dead pig is expensive in food, time and capital.

Inadequate housing can prove very expensive in that the pig may suffer from lack of appropriate shelter or from unhygienic conditions. Unsuitable doors, a generally insecure sty, or bad fencing may result in wasted hours at the most inopportune times chasing after escaped pigs. Pigs can easily become really smelly if not cleaned out regularly. A good soakaway is essential.

Some strains of pigs are more noisy than others and on hearing the feed bucket they may start screaming in anticipation; this can offend neighbours. Generally though, when kept in backyard numbers—i.e. just one or two—they are so content that one is usually only greeted by grunts of anticipation.

At the time of going to press, a pig reared entirely on purchased foodstuffs may well cost more than the market value of the fat carcase, but of course with the judicious use of the kitchen pig bucket—paying special attention to the regulations for the treatment of swill (see page 89)—augmented by next door's scraps (in exchange for a joint when slaughter time comes), it is surprising how cheaply our pigs can be fed in terms of actual cash spent. This method of feeding may take the pigs a little longer to fatten.

Of course, it all comes back to the fact that in order to rear pigs successfully we must *like* them, and of all the farm animals I think they are one of the most intelligent.

2 Buying Your Pigs

A couple of well-reared, strong weaners should lead you to a trouble-free initiation into the joys and delights of keeping pigs, and eventually to the pleasure of homegrown pork and bacon. One often hears of those who have been given runts, pippins, nisguards, wrecklings, caddies or parson's pigs, producing the largest pigs ever seen. But why not *begin* with strong, healthy piglets which have had a good start in life? In three months' time, with common sense and a dose of good luck, they will be adorning your kitchen table neatly jointed, packed and labelled ready for the deep-freeze. The healthy piglet is a constant source of fun and will be a pleasure to show off to friends.

Once experience has been gained with normally healthy stock this may be the time to indulge in rearing the weaker, smaller brethren. One becomes more observant: little changes in the animal's smell, temperature, skin colour and general demeanour are noticed almost before they happen. This ability to observe incipient trouble will be essential in the rearing of weaker stock as they will naturally be more likely to succumb to any adverse conditions.

Sources of Stock

Pig farmers. Generally the owners of larger pig units are loth to allow visitors for fear of introducing disease to the establishment. However, the smaller local pig farmer with but a few sows will often be pleased to show off his stock and may even be willing to sell a couple of strong weaners. If you can establish a friendly relationship he may also be helpful if problems occur, especially in the early days.

Advertisement. Your local newspaper may advertise pigs for sale under the heading 'Livestock'. These may often be animals from a one- or two-sow owner which have been reared in the type of surroundings in which you will have to keep your pigs.

Market. This is generally *not* the best way to buy a few pigs, as weaners are sold in litters or groups of about eight or more. It is a skilled job bidding against farmers and dealers who have often been doing this for many years. Also the risk of introducing infection from places such as markets can be far greater than when buying from a known source.

Buying runts

Some sows have too few teats or even insufficient milk for their litters (they *can* produce twenty or more live piglets in one litter). Unless the standard of management is very high, growth in the young is uneven and at least one will fail to grow as quickly as its litter mates merely through lack of sufficient milk. (Each

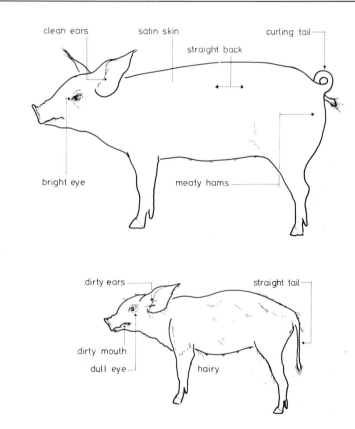

clean ears   satin skin   curling tail

straight back

bright eye   meaty hams

dirty ears   straight tail

dirty mouth
dull eye   hairy

Fig. 2 Well-grown weaner and runt from same litter.

piglet has its own teat, the strongest in the litter feeding from those near the head of the pig and the weaker from those nearer the tail.) If the number of piglets exceeds the teats available, the weaker youngsters will naturally have to take second place. As the sow only 'lets down' her milk for a very limited period those with no room at the milk bar get little or no milk, as they will have to struggle for the leavings after the others have drunk. These supernumerary pigs, though possibly perfectly normal otherwise, fail to grow as fast as the rest of the litter. Ad-lib early weaning pellets in a creep-feed hopper (which the sow cannot reach) and *easy* access to plenty of fresh, clean water will help to remedy the situation. In spite of this treatment, however, some piglets will fail to grow at a normal rate.

These animals bought at eight weeks or so (possibly half the weight of their siblings), housed in roomy, clean, dry and warm surroundings and fed an adequate diet *can* begin to put on weight at a phenomenal rate. This is known as compensatory growth. However they may well tend to put on fat unless great care is exercised. Milk from a house cow, or better still goat's milk, will transform these pipkins from grubby, lean and hairy runts into clean, sleek and lively, healthy piglets.

Success in rearing depends on attention to detail. It is worth obtaining a good-quality creep feed which can be fed as pellets in a shallow trough. The milk can then be fed in a separate trough away from the pellet container to avoid possible sourness or rancidity. Fresh pellets given daily will ensure optimum consumption. There must also be a trough of clean water available which is not large enough for the piglets to wallow in but low enough for them to reach easily. The milk trough must be cleaned thoroughly between each feed to prevent sourness developing. I like to give these pigs two milk feeds a day, allowing just enough milk for them to finish greedily. Any remaining milk must be removed, fed to older stock, and the trough thoroughly cleaned. While goat's milk will rarely result in stomach upsets as it is very readily digested, cow's milk must be diluted to a mixture of half water and half whole milk at first, gradually increasing to all whole milk over the period of a week.

Underfeeding milk is preferable to overfeeding as this is less likely to overload the digestion. It is best not to introduce skim or separated milk until the animals are seen to be really thriving as it is not a balanced feed and is thus not so easily digested. Once the pigs are clean, shining and obviously glowing with health a cheaper rearing meal can be introduced or even barley meal and milk (see page 46).

Quantities of milk are difficult to stipulate as the size of runts at weaning may vary enormously. A healthy 25 kg weaner can take up to 2 litres of separated milk a day. A baconer can consume 4 litres, this being fed with as much barley meal as the pig will thoroughly clear in twenty minutes (see page 46).

Early weaners

Some pig units now wean their piglets at three to four weeks of age or even earlier in order to fit in one more litter per sow, per year. I feel that stock bought for home rearing at so young an age is best avoided at the early stages, until more experience has been gained in pig rearing. Unless one is aware of signs of stress the animals may take *months* longer to fatten than the conventional six- to eight-week weaner.

Abnormal pigs

Hernias. Piglets exhibiting an abnormality but which may still be worth rearing are those with either scrotal hernias (in hog pigs) or umbilical hernias in either hogs or gilts. The scrotal hernia may possibly be sewn by a vet at castration but the umbilical hernia is best left alone. We have found that piglets with umbilical hernias can survive and the condition may possibly even be reduced with dry meal feeding and avoidance of too much roughage—grass, cabbage, etc (wet mash may aggravate the problem severely). It is only worth bothering with these piglets if they are *really* cheap and are going to be reared with only one other pig, as one wants to avoid any damage to the animal which could prove fatal. Ensure that there are no jutting corners on which the pig could catch the pro-truberance. A round water trough is helpful here with the food thrown directly on the floor to cut down the number of sharp edges in the pen.

Blind piglets. These will survive when kept in very small numbers where there is little or no competition. The condition may have been caused by lack of vitamin A in the parent.

Trembling pigs. This is a condition which normally disappears by weaning age. We have reared them successfully. They tend to lie about more than normal stock. The quiet surroundings and adequate feed space found in the backyard sty give these pigs a chance to fatten normally. The shivering can be quite violent and in this case it may impede the normal rate of feeding.

Deformities of the jaw and nose. Under- or over-shot jaws (where the two jaws do not meet normally at the snout) need not affect the ability of the backyard pig to feed. Wet feeding will be most suitable here with a trough that is deep enough to allow the animal to get hold of sufficient food. Occasionally a pig is born with an excessively upturned snout. Again, deep wide troughs must be available for feeding. An automatic drinker will not be any use for this type of pig as it will not be able to get its mouth into the bowl to drink.

It is wisest not to embark on these second-grade pigs unless you feel *really* confident. If they are given to you and you have the time, space and experience they can prove profitable. On the other hand the chance of them dying, having in the meantime eaten a lot of expensive food (the ones with hernias will need conventional pig-meal feeding), will be much higher than one might normally expect.

In twenty years of rearing both runt and normal backyard pigs we have lost only one and this was found on post-mortem examination to have a faulty heart, though on purchase it appeared perfectly normal. Reasonable care and attention and not a little luck will result in rearing all your stock to slaughter-weight. Runts will however often take longer to reach maturity.

Pitfalls to avoid when buying stock

Obviously there are pitfalls in buying runts. Piglets recovering from pneumonia may be left with per-manently damaged lungs and you will have difficulty detecting this at purchase. Animals which have suffered from erysipelas may show abnormal growths in the heart on post-mortem examination.

They may also develop varying difficulties in walking caused by progressive arthritis. Poor growth may have been caused by an excessive worm burden and these worm-ridden stock will infect your prem-ises. All this shows that it is well worth buying your stock from people you know and trust, but do remember that rearing runts is always a gamble and could possibly be an absolute dead loss.

Bringing them home

Once the pigs are purchased bring them home and quietly put them in the sty. In winter a temporary hutch can be built of straw bales to keep the newcomers really warm and compensate for loss of their mother's and siblings' warmth. A plentiful supply of straw in one corner will suffice in warm weather, leaving one or two rams of straw unshaken so that the pigs can rootle about for odd bits of grain. Make sure the water trough is full of clean, fresh water. Now go away and leave them quietly for an hour or so. It's a good plan to buy a bag of food from the farmer from whom you purchased the pigs and to which they have been accustomed, and only gradually introduce your own. Give a small feed the first evening, using the same method as that with which they have been familiar, e.g. wet or dry etc.

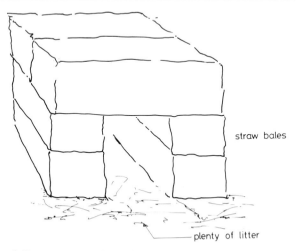

straw bales

plenty of litter

Fig. 3 Temporary warm hutch for new weaners.
By the time they are accustomed to the new surroundings they will no longer need the hutch and the bales can be used for litter.

They will be very shy at first, emitting only short, sharp grunts. Talk to them as you approach and they will soon associate your voice with food and pleasure. Their tails may well hang down straight for the first day or two but will soon assume a jaunty curl as they settle down. As they become accustomed to their new surroundings, slowly increase the feed to an amount which they will consume and clear with avidity within about a quarter of an hour. Keep a sharp eye open for the shape and texture of the droppings (see page 72) and note the general smell of the house first thing in the morning. Watch the general demeanour and brightness of the pigs (see page 71).

Flies. We have found that during July and August especially, the problem of insects (particularly flies) may assume uncomfortable proportions. If at all possible it may be sensible to take the opportunity to have a rest from pigs during this period. When the pigs have been slaughtered, scrub out the buildings thoroughly using Jeyes' Fluid or a similar product, according to instructions, having removed all straw and dung. There is not a lot known about resting buildings but it has been found that animals living in buildings that have been used for that purpose continuously will fail to thrive as well as those which live in buildings which are rested at intervals. The bad fly period can be an excuse for resting the buildings. By September (in England at least) the problem will not be nearly so bad.

Castration

Normally, male pigs will have been castrated before they are sold as weaners. It is not absolutely necessary to do this as the pig will not reach sexual maturity until after it has reached slaughter-weight and so there is little risk of boar taint in the flesh.

Before embarking on the castration of young male pigs, watch and help an experienced operator. It would be *most* unwise to attempt the operation without sufficient guidance.

A simple method of restraining a small piglet (if there is no extra help at hand) is to place the animal head first in a suitably sized wellington boot, holding the boot firmly between the knees.

Housing

The last hundred years have seen a vast amount of work on the 'improvement' of pigs. The forest pig, which was largely self-supporting, made its own nest in the undergrowth and fed on roots, tree seeds, such as acorns and beech mast, interspersed with grazing. This animal was extremely hardy and hairy, grew relatively slowly and had but a short back and small hams. However, the modern hybrid has short, sparse hair, meaty hind legs (hams) and a long back (many back rashers). During the process of improvement much of the hardiness may have been lost, but we now have an extremely meaty animal which quickly converts relatively little food into meat.

The modern breeds will not easily survive without good, snug housing. Many of the pigs to be seen in large pig units are carefully bred 'hybrids' which can be very profitable when kept in the ideal conditions created by relatively expensive housing. The more traditional breeds like the Tamworth, the Gloucester Old Spot, the Large Black and the Saddleback are still hardy and do not require special conditions; thriving when kept out of doors with access to simple housing, they are able to rear their young without the aid of supplementary heat.

Adapting existing buildings

Many houses in the country boast of at least one shud (as we call them in Norfolk). Obviously a wooden shed made from secondhand timber and roofed with corrugated iron will not withstand the hefty shoulder and questing snout of our backyard pig. However, the range of brick outhouses lurking behind even the humblest older country cottage can often be adapted into a pig sty, especially if it is not too near the house—in summer flies can be a problem. A brick brew-house or shed where the clothes boiler was housed may be adequate with a little modification and repair after a critical over-all look at the building from roof to foundations.

Roof. Check this on the first wet day to see where rain is coming in. Individual tiles may have to be replaced, and, if there are no spares, it will be necessary to find a course or two of closely matching tiles using the old

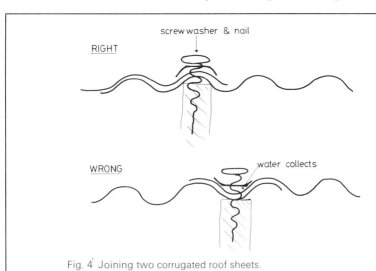

Fig. 4 Joining two corrugated roof sheets.

ones for spares. It is worth replacing corroded metal guttering with modern plastic as this needs no upkeep. Corrugated-iron roofing is best cleaned with a wire brush and then repainted as the rusting process continues if left under paint. If the corrugated sheeting is beyond repair, asbestos cement sheeting is expensive but quick to lay and needs no maintenance. Remember to use crawling boards or a ladder when working on a roof and avoid breathing in the dust if sawing is necessary.

Walls. A brick building which has been neglected for many years may need repointing. Rake out the joints, then brush and moisten to create a good key for the new mortar. Older buildings especially will not need a strong mixture: cement 1 part, lime 2 parts and sand 9 parts will be satisfactory if one is working in the spring or summer; in exposed positions or in the winter, cement 1 part, lime 1 part and sand 9 parts will be suitable. It is disastrous to use too strong a mixture—I have seen half a wall fall out in one piece after it had been knocked where this was done. The repair mixture was just too strong! Rat holes should be sealed with fine concrete.

Cobbled walls provide ideal harbours for bacteria—a good plan is to give the inside walls a facing of smooth cement.

Doors. Old ones are often basically very strong but showing their age. The lower parts of doors can be given a new lease of life and made pig-proof with galvanised steel or aluminium sheeting. (The decayed bases of old door frames can have new timbers spliced onto the old.) The hinges will often respond amazingly to vigorous wire brushing and a dose of penetrating oil. On old buildings these hinges were often handmade and, with a little attention, will last

27

many more years. Good new ones are very expensive.

Foundations. It may be worthwhile laying a one-metre-wide concrete path outside the building above the foundations or footings of brick walls, for added strength and trouble-free working.

Ceilings. A false ceiling can be erected very simply to keep the building snug for pigs.

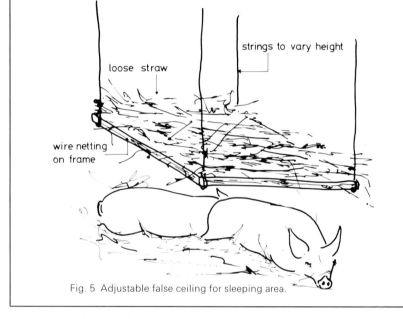

strings to vary height

loose straw

wire netting on frame

Fig. 5 Adjustable false ceiling for sleeping area.

Floors. A floor area of a minimum size of 2 × 2 metres will house a couple of fatteners adequately. (Pigs kept indoors spend about 80 per cent of the time lying on the floor.) Pigs have extremely strong snouts (watch the next pig you see in a field. If it has no ring in its nose it will leave a series of furrows behind it in its quest for food and worms.) We inherited a thin

28

concrete floor which cracked after twenty years of use. This was transformed by one particularly vigorous pig into a series of deep pits which has necessitated completely relaying the whole floor. It is worth spending a little time and money to ensure a strong, pig-proof and warm floor.

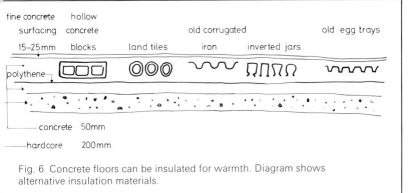

Fig. 6 Concrete floors can be insulated for warmth. Diagram shows alternative insulation materials.

Larger buildings. These can be divided off using concrete or cement blocks as dividing walls. We find existing buildings can be divided by 3-metre-long partitions which provide an adequate area for most needs. Spare compartments can be used for litter storage or as a food store provided the door is animal-proof (pig-fattening meals contain a certain amount of copper which can be fatal to goats or sheep if they gorge themselves). Internal walls five blocks high will be adequate and will allow good ventilation within the building.

Cement. Remember to buy only sufficient cement for the particular job as it quickly deteriorates when the bag is opened, particularly if conditions are at all damp. Sand can be delivered most cheaply from your nearest supplier as the cost lies mainly in the

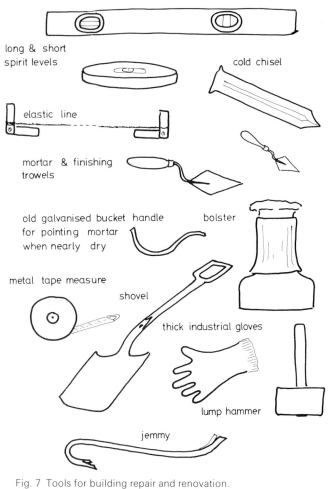

long & short spirit levels

cold chisel

elastic line

mortar & finishing trowels

old galvanised bucket handle for pointing mortar when nearly dry

bolster

metal tape measure

shovel

thick industrial gloves

lump hammer

jemmy

Fig. 7 Tools for building repair and renovation.

transport. A cubic metre is usually the least amount that they will deliver. Use washing-up liquid as an aid to mixing and to induce a 'fluffiness' to the mix. Proprietary brands of conditioner can be purchased and one drop per gallon of mixing water seems to be about right.

Dry-mix the cement, sand and lime thoroughly on an old piece of hardboard if there is no flat, clean surface available, and then hollow out the centre of the mix into which water can be poured. Mixing is then continued by filling in the hollow from the edges until the water has been absorbed. The mix is then turned and more water added until a firm mortar has been achieved.

Concrete blocks. Blocks are suitable for inside walls; the hollow ones are easiest to lay since they are wider but more mortar will be needed as it falls into the cavities during laying. It is well worth making sure that the foundations are absolutely level before you start, while to make the walls easy to clean the blocks can be rendered with a wet mix of 1 part cement to 3 parts coarse sand. An added luxury would be to round out the angle between wall and floor. It is vital to plan any door posts, boltholes or pen dividers *before* the walls are built as subsequent cold chiselling is arduous and may weaken the structure. Remember not to mix more mortar than you can use in about two hours.

Don't put a big pig into newly built concrete-block housing for at least ten weeks, when the mortar should be well set. Buttress single block walls every 3 metres

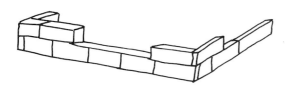

Fig. 8 Order of block laying.

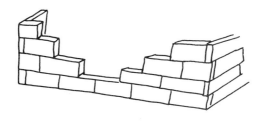

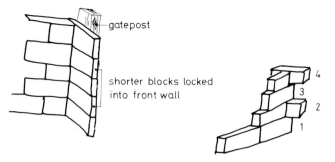

gatepost

shorter blocks locked
into front wall

4
3
2
1

Fig. 9 Gatepost put beside buttress on wall for greater strength.
Fig. 10 Laying blocks against an existing wall without keying into
older wall.

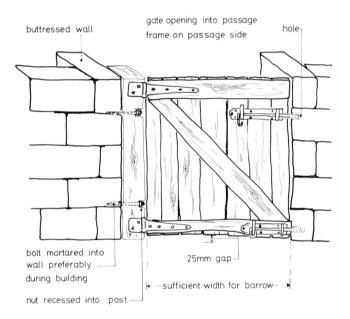

buttressed wall

gate opening into passage
frame on passage side

hole

bolt mortared into
wall preferably
during building

nut recessed into post

25mm gap

sufficient width for barrow

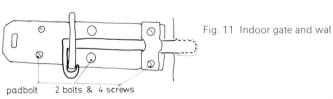

Fig. 11 Indoor gate and wal

padbolt   2 bolts & 4 screws

or so. Do not leave the ends of walls unbuttressed as they are only as strong as the mortar holding them together.

Purpose-built accommodation

Without existing buildings one has the luxury of planning a purpose-built piggery. If only a couple of fatteners are to be kept at any one time, a simple cottage-type sty can be erected and this will not normally need planning permission as it will only be supplying household quantities of meat. If in doubt it is just as well to enquire from the local district council before you start the enterprise. If permission is not required building may commence, not forgetting that certain building regulations may have to be adhered to. If on the other hand building permission is required, apply to the district council. If this is refused, an appeal can be made but this may take six months or longer to be heard.

The cottage sty rears a hardy pig and is easy to clean. Most pigs are very fastidious, keeping their sleeping quarters dry and only dunging in one spot—outside if possible. This type of housing has a low roof making for snug, warm sleeping and resting quarters.

Pigs, especially the older breeds, can be kept out of doors provided that they have access to housing for warmth and shelter. These animals enjoy plenty of

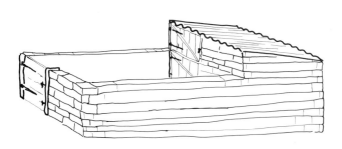

Fig. 12 Block-built cottage-style sty.

fresh air and are thus less susceptible to respiratory infection. They can get plenty of exercise and will rarely be short of minerals which they will be able to obtain from the soil. One saves on the food bill and housing is cheap. However, they will have to survive the hazards of rain, wind and snow and the consequent mud, and more time may have to be spent looking after them in the resulting less congenial conditions. Carting food, water and litter in a heavy rainstorm may test even the hardiest member of the family.

Outdoor housing

Simple housing can be erected from six curved corrugated-iron sheets with a central post for rigidity. The back can be filled in with timber and set into the prevailing wind.

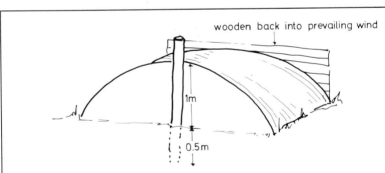

wooden back into prevailing wind

1m

0.5m

Fig. 13 Corrugated-iron field shelter. Wooden end into prevailing wind; extra post to support front.

Apex arks. These are very suitable for a breeding sow. The angle of the floor with the walls will provide ample protection for the young against being overlain. The ark will take the pigs from birth to about 35 kg. If used for accommodating fattening pigs it will adequately house two animals to slaughter-weight.

34

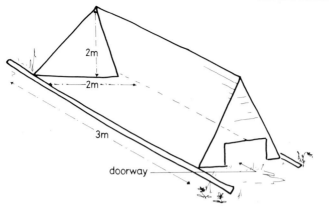

Fig. 14 Apex ark. This can be used for weaners or for a tethered sow and litter.

When the ark needs to be moved, a tractor will be required, or two strong adults.

Straw bales. A really cheap building can be erected of straw. When the house is old it can be burnt to destroy vermin and lice. However, there is a high fire risk. The advantages are its cheapness, speed of building and the fact that the next one can be erected in a new place to prevent the surroundings becoming foul.

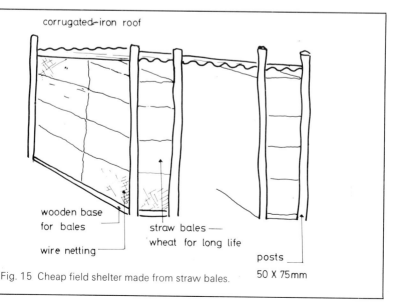

Fig. 15 Cheap field shelter made from straw bales.

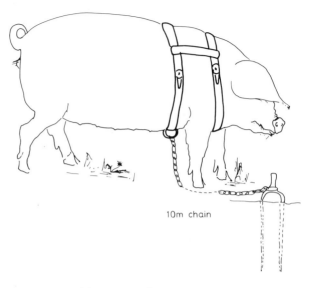

Fig. 16 Tether for older rearers and sows.

10m chain

Restraint

Pigs kept in outdoor housing will obviously need restraining in some way or other. An adult pig (a breeder) can be harnessed or tethered in such a way as to enable her to graze and to gain access to her shelter. However, smaller pigs will resent this method. They will need fencing of some kind.

Fencing

Woven-wire pig netting. This is generally available in rolls 50 m. long and 1 m. high. The bottom and top wires are generally gauge 9 with intermediate wires less thick. The strength of this fencing lies in the efficiency of the posts, which need to be not more than 3 m. apart with very strong straining posts. This type of netting is often obtainable at farm sales but do remember to check prices of new rolls before you go. Odd rolls of netting at farm sales are often *not* the full

36

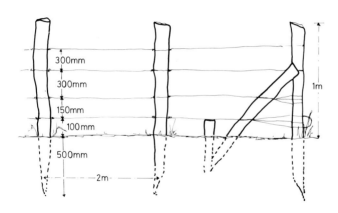

Fig. 17 Pig netting.

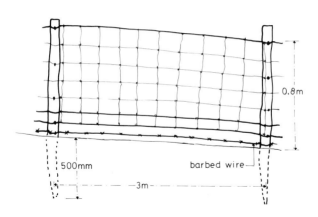

Fig. 18 Chestnut-post fence. Wire must be well strained.

length. Check the condition of the galvanising as the life of the netting will be considerably shortened once rust has set in.

Chestnut posts. A cheaper, mobile and therefore more adaptable fencing consists of chestnut posts set 2 m.

apart (split chestnut posts do not rot and will stand being moved). We have some *riven* (split along the natural grain) chestnut posts which are continually being moved and these are at least forty years old. They do not require creosoting. Heavy gauge wire is essential.

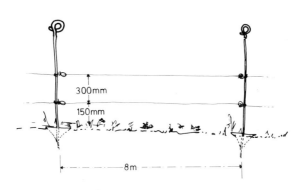

Fig. 19 Electric fencing using metal fence posts.

Electric fencing. As the pig has less hair than most animals it readily feels the shock. It is advisable to teach the animals by first putting them in a small fenced area so that they will quickly come into contact with the electric wire. The success of this type of fencing relies on at least once-daily checking, taking along a spade and shears. Any soil thrown up against the wire by the pigs will earth the current. Herbage of any kind, especially when it is wet, will cause a leakage and thus reduce any shock.

Mobile fold units. This may not strictly be classed as fencing but on the other hand a well-made fold unit will efficiently confine the pigs and house them at the same time. Success is really only possible where just one or two pigs are housed, otherwise the run will quickly become fouled. The unit must be moved daily and therefore must necessarily be strongly built. Such structures are both expensive and heavy.

4 Feeding

Under conventional pig-farming conditions food will represent about 80 per cent of the cost of fattening a pig. Where many pigs are kept, particular types of ration which will bring the pigs to slaughter-weight even a few days sooner than others will represent a considerable saving. However, when keeping a mere couple of pigs, these savings may be barely noticeable.

The economies that the backyard pig keeper can employ are the utilisation of household waste (see page 89 for laws relating to swill feeding) and the use of homegrown foods, greengrocer's and baker's waste. These last two do *not* qualify as swill as they have not been in contact with meat. Fish and chip swill is also excellent if there are *no chicken or other meat products on the same premises*.

Initially I feel that it may be best for the newcomer to pig keeping to feed his first pig or two using conventional miller's rations, as these are fairly foolproof and the experience gained from seeing a normal, strong, healthy weaner growing fast and efficiently may prove good background experience and also give an idea of what you are aiming to produce. I have seen a newcomer ploughing on stoically with his first solitary runt, not realising that the poor little creature was suffering from chronic mange, malnutrition and general unthriftiness. He seemed to forget that the animal should have taken

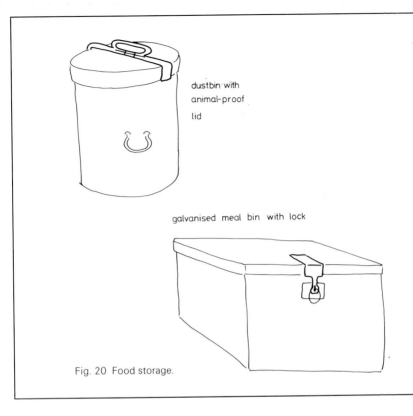

dustbin with
animal-proof
lid

galvanised meal bin with lock

Fig. 20 Food storage.

half the time to fatten and though it appeared cheerful enough I'm sure it must have made rather tough eating.

Conventional rations from a reliable miller will contain carbohydrates, proteins, vitamins and minerals in the correct proportions for the appropriate age and weight of animal. These are supplied as small pellets in the case of a creep ration and as larger nuts for older stock. For breeding stock living out of doors, jumbo-sized nuts too big for birds to carry away are useful but feeding can also be done by means of meal.

Forms of feed

Meal. This can be fed *dry*. Some like to feed directly on to a clean floor but this can be rather a wasteful

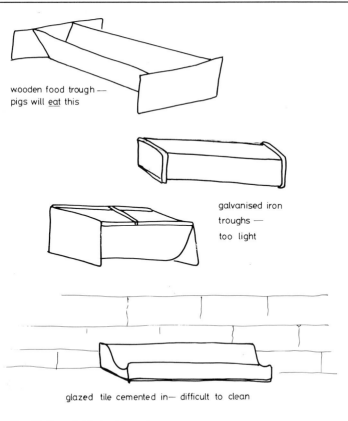

wooden food trough —
pigs will <u>eat</u> this

galvanised iron
troughs —
too light

glazed tile cemented in— difficult to clean

Fig. 21 Unsuitable feed troughs.

method and is unhygienic. If meal is fed *wet*, aim at a thick, sloppy consistency. Take care that the troughs are kept scrupulously clean, particularly if milk is used, as the liquid or the old, souring milk may cause stomach upsets. Wet mash is more appetising than dry meal and is easier to digest (wet-mash feeding is not suitable for a pig with a hernia; here dry meal or cube feeding is essential—see page 21).

Cubes. These can be fed directly on to the floor or preferably in troughs. There is little or no waste but it

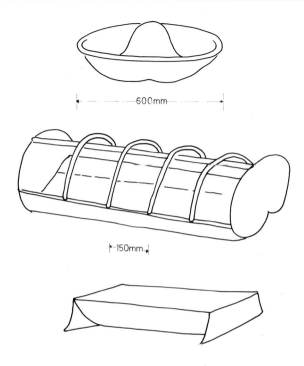

Fig. 22 Suitable cast-iron water and feed troughs, too heavy for pigs to move. They can be bought at farm sales very cheaply and help to prevent anaemia into the bargain.

is important to have fresh, clean water available at all times.

Ad-lib feeding versus restricted feeding

Ad-lib feeding.

1. Where meal is available twenty-four hours a day, only a dry meal system is suitable.
2. Gives better growth rates than rationed feeding but it is difficult to see when an animal is off its feed.
3. May allow the animal to put on too much back fat in the later stages of fattening.

Restricted feeding.

1. Usually two meals daily, the exception being when you have some very poor, small pigs which may need a third feed.
2. Allows the feeder to judge the appetite of the pigs.
3. Allows the fatness of the pig to be controlled.
4. May cause fighting if there is not enough trough space for all the animals to feed at once comfortably.
5. Is most successful when animals are fed regularly at the same times each day, e.g. 7.00 am and 6.00 pm.

used household food tins.

Fig. 23 Method of feed measuring.

Water

Whatever method of feeding is employed the importance of water *cannot be underestimated*. An animal can survive days without food but will quickly die without water because:

1. Water is the medium by which much body temperature regulation occurs.
2. It is one of the components of many essential body secretions.
3. Nutrients are carried round the body largely dissolved in water.

4. Water is passed out when the animal breathes and urinates. A pig will need about 3 litres of water for every 1 kg of meal fed, though this may fall as fattening proceeds. A lactating sow will need up to 20 litres daily when suckling her young.

Bulky foods

When feeding homegrown foods, try to aim at as wide a variety of materials being fed each day as possible. This will ensure that there are sufficient vitamins and minerals in the ration.

Grass. Very leafy spring grass is obviously more digestible than the grazing available in late summer. The advantage gained from spring grass may be lost by the frantic search for fibrous, low-value July grasses. However, the pig kept under a grazing system will often look far healthier and happier than his indoor counterpart and may be less likely to suffer from mineral deficiencies.

Russian Comfrey. A well-manured crop (and comfrey thrives on uncomposted, fresh pig manure!) will provide more low-fibre and good-quality protein per

Fig. 24 Four-legged ploughing. Fence unringed pigs on piece of land to be cleared of weeds.

hectare than most other forage plants. It is also highly palatable to pigs, though chickens, goats and horses prefer it wilted at first and need a little encouragement to eat it. Once a weaner weighs 50 kg or so and is eating about $1\frac{1}{2}$ kg of fattening meal a day, comfrey can be fed to appetite. $2\frac{1}{2}$ kg of fresh comfrey will replace $\frac{1}{2}$ kg of fattening meal. Newly weaned pigs will require the young leaves which are low in fibre while the older ones will eat the dry, older part of the comfrey plant. One drawback is that this plant crops only during the summer months, the first cut being taken in April and the last in September. Pigs can be folded over it once the area is established after two or three years. Lawrence Hills' book *Comfrey, Past, Present and Future* gives full details for feeding and cultivation.

Kale. It is worth growing the variety Maris Kestrel as a winter succulent for pigs but it must be fed in moderation. They will trample it underfoot if folded over it and are inclined to waste the rather fibrous stems and roots. However one stem twice a day once the pigs reach 50 kg will prove a valuable extra.

Fodder Beet. The variety Red Ottofte is an excellent winter bulk feed and has the highest dry matter of all the fodder-beet varieties.

Potatoes. Chat potatoes, unsprouted and boiled (which makes them more digestible), form a low-fibre carbohydrate and can replace a certain amount of fattening meal. It is considered wise to throw away the cooking water.

Artichokes. If grown on a fertile soil these vegetables can crop really well. They can be left to be rooted out by the pigs during the winter—the tops having been cut for green feed for goats or rabbits during the summer. Too much artichoke is inclined to produce offensive-smelling, dark dung.

Greengrocer's waste. Pigs seem to enjoy most fruit and vegetables but experience has shown that amongst those things that they do not appreciate are onions, lemons and grapefruit; too many oranges may cause diarrhoea. The traditional unimproved breeds, notably the Tamworth and Gloucester Old Spot, will enjoy such food in moderation, but it is wise to feed these wastes in very small quantities and with great circumspection at first to the modern 'hybrid' type of pig in order to avoid digestive upsets.

Milk

Separated milk is a top-quality protein food but is rarely available to the backyarder unless he has his own cow or goat.

Allow 2 litres of separated milk at weaning. This can gradually be increased to 4 litres at slaughter-weight. Great care must be taken to see that milk is always fed fresh, the feeding troughs being thoroughly cleaned daily. Some pig keepers feed skim milk watered down 1 part water to 1 part skim, but I have found that if the proportion of milk is gradually increased over a period of ten days or so there will be no problem. I have reared and fattened pigs purely on a diet of barley meal mixed with milk, using as much barley meal as the animals would finish in twenty minutes. Odd vegetables and cabbage leaves were fed as available.

General hints on feeding

If feeding conventional miller's rations, be guided by the manufacturer's instructions as to quantities.

Remember that if a pig is eager for his feed he

probably needs all he is being offered. If he ambles up waiting for his back to be scratched, then cut his ration by a half for that feed. If he's not bothered about his food at all, miss out that feed altogether. Keep a sharp eye on him but as likely as not his appetite will have returned by the next feed time. Always allow an ample supply of fresh water at all times under whatever system the pig is fed or kept.

Feed *regularly*—i.e. at the same times each day.

Rules for conventional ration feeding

1. Allow at least ten days for changeover from one ration to another, mixing progressively more of the new ration with the old until the final change is made.
2. Do not necessarily go for the cheapest ration. Decide on a reliable miller and be guided by his recommendations.

In these days of expensive miller's rations many people are finding that they can fatten their household pigs using the minimum of proprietary products. Depending on the availability, ease and cheapness of obtaining it, foodstuffs like baker's and greengrocer's waste can augment the household scraps and possible spare milk.

In order that our pig will grow adequately he must have sufficient protein in his diet. As he gets older and reaches over 50 kg in weight he can fatten adequately on a much lower level of protein. His vitamin and mineral requirements will be taken care of if he has a certain amount of fresh greenstuff daily and, if he is kept indoors, a daily shovelful of fresh earth from a pig-free area (to avoid the risk of soil-borne diseases and worm larvae) will help to prevent anaemia.

A convenient system of feeding which ensures a good start with adequate protein, is to feed the ration to which he was accustomed before weaning (creep or sow and weaner) until he weighs about 25 kg. This will gradually be changed to a rearing ration, feeding about 1 kg per day. Thereafter keep to this daily quantity of meal but allow him as much bulky food with his meals as he will clear up if he lives indoors, i.e. scraps, cabbage, etc, or grazing and vegetable wastes if kept outdoors. When feeding household scraps take care not to include salt off the sides of plates as this can poison the animal.

> . . . the fattening of a large hog yields three or four load of dung . . . it is much in small space, it makes no show as flocks and herds do, but without it the cultivation of the land would be a poor, a miserably barren concern.
>
> William Cobbett

Table 1 Rough rationing guide using balanced meal for growing and finishing pigs

Live weight of pig	Daily ration
20 kg	1·5 kg
30 kg	1·75 kg
40 kg	2·0 kg
50 kg	2·5 kg
60 kg	3·0 kg
70 kg	3·25 kg

Table 2 Rough estimate of equivalent energy values

1 kg barley meal
4 kg cooked potatoes
5 kg sugar-beet pulp
5 kg fodder beet
7·5 kg kale
10 kg grass

Breeds and Breeding

The majority of backyard pig keepers are thankful to obtain pigs whatever the breed. The fact that they have lop ears means they may travel in a straight line if they get free; our prick-eared pigs may look more intelligent than some when we talk to them. The extra pound or so of bacon which we can obtain from a Landrace pig will be a bonus while there's no real reason why we shouldn't grow a Middle White on (it's normally kept for pork) until it reaches bacon-weight.

Breeds can be differentiated by their rates of maturing. Obviously the commercial pig farmer carefully studies his market, decides on the breed which suits his particular trade, then houses and feeds the animals accordingly.

Early maturing, suitable for pork	Berkshire Middle White
Dual purpose	British Saddleback Large Black Gloucester Old Spot
Late maturing, suitable for bacon	Landrace Large White Tamworth Welsh

As far as the backyard man is concerned the most important thing is to know roughly what the breed is. For example, he would not buy a Landrace pig and leave it out in the woods during the late summer and autumn expecting it to fatten or even survive. On the other hand it would be a waste of money for him to build expensive, well-insulated, exotically ventilated housing for a Tamworth pig.

Traditional breeds

Here are some examples of older breeds that are still fairly easily obtainable and which are hardy scavengers and good mothers:

Gloucester Old Spot. These are white with black spots or patches. The sows are excellent mothers and milkers and live long, useful breeding lives. Often they are crossed with a Welsh boar to produce very acceptable weaners for the market.

Large Black. They have a black skin. The pigs are hardy and flourish on an extensive system while the sows have good mothering qualities.

Tamworth. These pigs have a golden brown skin with ginger hair. They are slower to fatten than many other breeds but they are good scavengers and thrive outside.

The British Saddleback. Black pigs with a white waistband and lop ears. Excellent grazers and very docile. Thrive when kept intensively as well as extensively.

Other British breeds

Those pigs which will thrive under more intensive systems are the *Welsh* — white with lop ears; the *Berkshire* — black with a white flash on a dished nose; *Middle White* and *Large White*.

The Landrace. A Danish import, this is a lop-eared, long-backed, white pig. They have been very highly bred, are lean and prolific and thrive when kept in expensive housing under ideal management. They have been used to revolutionise our British breeds.

There are other breeds being imported but these may not commonly be available.

Hybrid pigs

These are the product of planned cross-breeding. They may be heavier at weaning than some and produce more lean meat at a faster rate and from less food. Generally though, they are not the product of the hardier breeds and so will need ideal housing and the best miller's rations to take full advantage of their breeding.

As I mentioned earlier the backyarder would be well advised to find a reliable, trustworthy source of weaners which suits his system of housing and feeding and also is readily available locally. Household quantities of pork and bacon will *easily* be supplied by the occasional pair of weaners.

Breeding considered

Breeding involves a lot of know-how, expensive housing for the improved, modern breeds and extensive grazing and scavenging areas to take full advantage of breeds like the Large Black, Gloucester Old Spot, Tamworth and British Saddleback. There is the problem of finding a boar (it would be an extremely expensive luxury to keep one for only a sow or two), the difficulties presented by the restrictions on the movement of animals and the problem of disease transmission which makes boar owners loth to have visiting sows—even if there *is* a local boar of your choice and breed. However, there are artificial insemination facilities available but the conception rate is not yet as good as using a boar. On the other hand AI makes available to you the very best boars at not too great a cost.

If you *do* decide to take the plunge and breed your

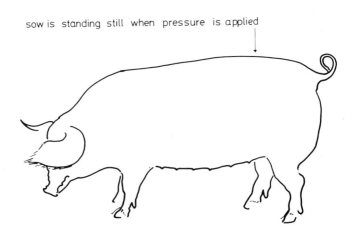

sow is standing still when pressure is applied

Fig. 25 Testing a sow for heat.

sow, a good temperament is vital; a flighty sow who eats her young is useless. Choose a good, milky strain with at least fourteen teats and good mothering capabilities. In a book designed to show how to grow a rasher of bacon there is not room to go into the finer points of breeding; however, the following points may be of interest.

Readiness for mating

A gilt may become sexually mature at five months but wait till she is about eight months before serving her, in order to allow her to grow. The heat cycle is around twenty-one days throughout the year, the heat lasting from eight to thirty-six hours. Some females will display a swollen vulva as well as being restless when on heat, while others may only be slightly off their food. However, if she stands still when pressure is applied to the loins this usually means she is ready for the boar. Do see that she is handled as quietly as possible during this period and feed her well.

Mating

Copulation takes longer than for many animals, the boar taking anything up to twenty minutes to complete the service. If a large boar is used on a young gilt it may be necessary to put her in a service crate to prevent her being damaged by the excessive weight of the boar. Around three weeks after she has been served, watch her carefully for signs of desiring to return to the boar. Gestation lasts just under four months.

Feeding an in-pig sow

An in-pig sow having access to grazing will need about 2 kg of sow and weaner ration per day. The aim is to supply her needs without allowing her to become either overfat or thin and poor. Again, see she has as much fresh, clean water as she needs (grazing in the hot sun is very thirsty work).

Where comfrey is fed it may be economically advantageous to arrange things so that farrowing takes place at about the end of April, getting the benefit of the spring growth of comfrey. As comfrey is a high-protein food it can be fed ad lib, provided 1 kg of sow and weaner meal is fed daily. With this system the sow *may* look leaner than her sisters who are being fed a complete sow and weaner ration, but she will likely as not produce more young, milk better, rear better piglets and also 'come on store' (come on heat) earlier after the young are weaned.

Signs of farrowing

During the gestation period feed the sow with care, and if necessary cut it down a bit a week before farrowing so that she does not become overstocked (too full of milk) too soon. If she shows signs of constipation, gradually introduce up to 2 kg of bran mash to replace the sow and weaner ration. She may become restless and show signs of wanting to nest any time within three days of the expected date; also between twelve and twenty-four hours before farrowing, her teats will become obviously full of milk.

Farrowing

The sow will lie down to farrow, and once the first piglet is born the rest usually follow in quick succession. Each will break its own umbilical cord, then normally totter directly round to the milk bar. If the sow is distressed it is as well to take each piglet as it is born and put it in a box, then return them to her as soon as she's settled. Watch for the afterbirth as this may come away with the last piglet and can cause suffocation if not removed.

The young piglets drink frequently and quickly. A grunt from the mother as she settles down on her side, and they *all* rush to their teats and suck furiously for a minute or two. She then decides they've had enough and they go off to rest.

Commercial pig farmers have found that losses of piglets caused by sows squashing their young can be drastically reduced by housing the sows in metal farrowing crates (these can be obtained secondhand at farm sales). The sow is put in the crate a few days before the expected farrowing date and remains in it for about a fortnight after farrowing. Many breeders of the more traditional breeds do not find these crates necessary.

Detusking

Piglets have excessively sharp teeth. It may be necessary to tip their eye teeth and premolars with teeth pincers *before* they damage the sow's teats. Your vet can show you how to do this.

Feeding

Three days after farrowing, if all is well, the mother's

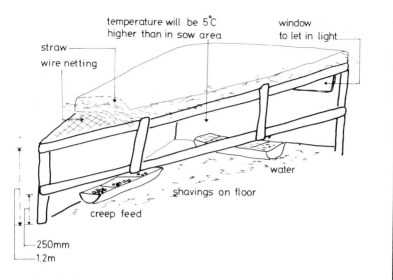

temperature will be 5°C higher than in sow area

window to let in light

straw

wire netting

water

shavings on floor

creep feed

250mm

1.2m

Fig. 26 Creep feed and warm area for young piglets born either inside or outside.

bran mash and sow and weaner ration can gradually be changed to sow and weaner alone. She will need 3 kg plus about 0.25 kg for each piglet. Do be guided by her condition. Don't be frightened to feed more than this if she's obviously poor, or cut down a bit if she's on the plump side and not keen to finish her food. *Don't forget her supply of fresh water.*

Weaning

This will normally take place (for the backyarder at least) at about six to eight weeks. Take the sow away from the piglets, if possible out of hearing of her young—the piglets will then be less likely to miss her. They will at this stage be well established on their creep ration but do see they have sufficient water.

Cut down the sow's ration drastically and limit her water supply, so that after forty-eight hours the skin behind the teats should look crinkly indicating that the milk source is drying up. With luck she will come on store within a few days.

The Rare Breeds Survival Trust, based at Winkleigh, Devonshire, publishes a monthly journal entitled *The Ark* which contains interesting articles and letters concerning the many aspects of maintaining the traditional breeds of farm livestock. Since the war many breeds have become extinct and valuable genetic material has thus been lost. The Trust arranges, among other things, displays of these breeds owned by Trust members at county agricultural shows, and does everything possible to maintain a general interest in their work.

6 The Harvest

One of the skills of rearing and fattening pigs is knowing *when* the animal is ready to kill. A pig-weighing machine is expensive; however there are tape measures on the market which are graduated in inches and which also show the corresponding weight in pounds when the tape is held round the pig's chest just behind the front leg and shoulder. It is reasonably accurate within a few pounds (there seem to be no metric ones about yet!), but of course the tape cannot estimate the fatness of the beast. It is a good idea to visit a market and feel the backs of the fat pigs due for slaughter. The amount of fat can roughly be gauged by the firmness of the flesh on the back just behind the shoulder. An animal which is too fat will feel soft whereas the leaner one will be firm to the touch but not boney. To give some idea of the weight of the final carcase in the old imperial measurements a score (20 lb) liveweight weighs a stone (14 lb) deadweight.

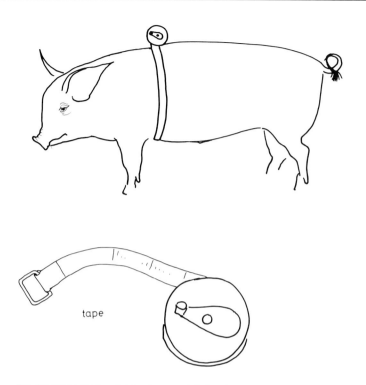

Fig. 27 Estimating weight using a weigh band.

Thus an 8-score (approximately 75 kg) live pig will weigh 8 stone (approximately 50 kg) dead—deadweight being the weight of the de-gutted carcase.

Treatment before slaughter

It is advisable to withhold all food for at least twelve hours before slaughter so that the gut is reasonably empty, but see that the water trough is clean and full of fresh water. Some slaughterhouses will want to have the pig on the premises the night before slaughter in which case the last meal will be the morning one. We find that the hungry backyard pig is easier to load as it will confidently follow its feeder on to the trailer to be rewarded by a handful of nuts or a favourite tit-bit.

Slaughterhouses

The law obliges us to have our pigs slaughtered on licensed premises where qualified meat inspectors from the local district council examine all carcases for signs of disease. Any meat which is unfit for human consumption is voluntarily surrendered under the Food and Drug Act of 1955. The most likely cause of failure in pigs will be a tubercular gland often found in the neck and this renders the head unusable. The body will be perfectly fit to eat.

It is worth finding out from pig-keeping friends which abattoirs happily take pigs for private slaughter and not too expensively. We have learned by bitter experience—there was the slaughterhouse which was loth to return the pluck (the liver, lights and heart), another which offered to do the butchery and returned only three trotters. Yet a third charged twice as much as any other slaughterhouse and would not even rive the carcase in half down the backbone.

Slaughterhouses start early in the morning and often finish work by 1.00 pm. They may close by 10.00 am on Saturdays (or even finish on Friday afternoons) for the weekend. Find out a convenient time to make yourself known (there is usually someone in the office at 10.00 am at the small slaughterhouse which we use). Explain what you would like done and ascertain when it would be convenient for them to slaughter your pig. If you co-operate with them they're likely to be more than helpful. Check that they have the space to hang the meat for a few days if it is going to be eaten fresh as pork. The bacon carcase will be best cooled at the slaughterhouse for only a day before being taken home for curing.

Transport

The boot of a car is not a suitable container for our fat pig, nor is the back of an estate car as it would not stand up to the gyrations of a frightened animal. We made a strong wooden crate which fitted into the back of our van, having been forced to adopt this method after we had tried to transport a pig loose in the back. The animal had desperately attempted first to assist the driver and failing this had tried to root the windows open. A pig or livestock trailer which can be hitched to a car is ideal, if the sides are high enough and built so that the animal cannot see through the boards. A roof is desirable to prevent draughts or undue exposure to the sun. Failing this there is usually a local carter who may be glad to earn a little extra by carting the odd pig to slaughter.

Loading

Pigs are loth to go into an unknown, dark area. The lop-eared ones are often easier to load as they seem to look ahead rather than to either side. Straw the floor of the trailer and place a small amount of litter from the pig's own pen on the ramp so that it will recognise its own smell. Give it a little time to sniff before firmly driving it up the ramp, having a solid board about 1 metre square on either side of it. Don't rush the animal or it will panic. Once it is frightened it is extremely difficult to get it actually on board without brutally manhandling it which can result in a badly bruised carcase. The aim is to get the pig to the slaughterhouse as calmly as possible, as it has been found that an animal badly frightened and not rested before killing may be tough to eat and the meat may be less successfully cured.

When unloading the animal it is often hesitant about coming out so tip the trailer up gently and the pig may then slowly sniff its way out. If the animal is determined not to get down pull it so that it lands on its back legs thus avoiding any damage. Mark the pen where the animal is left with your name and address stating clearly when you will collect the carcase. A waterproof pen mark on the animal's back will help the slaughterhouse staff. A tattooing 'slap' marker with your own code on it is expensive but will *ensure* that there is no mistake. The pins, which penetrate the skin, are impregnated with indelible ink which withstands the scalding and dehairing process.

Inspection

The inspection of meat is usually completed by midday (but this should be ascertained) so collect the pluck, which does not keep well and will need to be taken home as soon as possible. The carcase will have been stamped if it has passed the inspection. If the meat is to be cured it is best left at least six hours to cool and 'set' in the cold room. Pork however can be 'hung' for three days with advantage. Most slaughterhouses will do this for you but it is worth tactfully finding out when it is most convenient for you to collect the carcase. They will not appreciate having to stop work in order to load one solitary pig. It may be of interest to have the carcase weighed before you take it away and also have it riven down the back to assist the butcher at home! Some slaughterhouses will butcher the carcase for you for an extra fee if you do not feel confident to do the job yourself. We are lucky enough to have an excellent butcher friend who cuts our meat for us on our kitchen table. However, if you are selling the meat, it must be butchered on official, inspected premises.

Butchery

At the slaughterhouse. If someone at the slaughterhouse is going to butcher your pig, give him clear

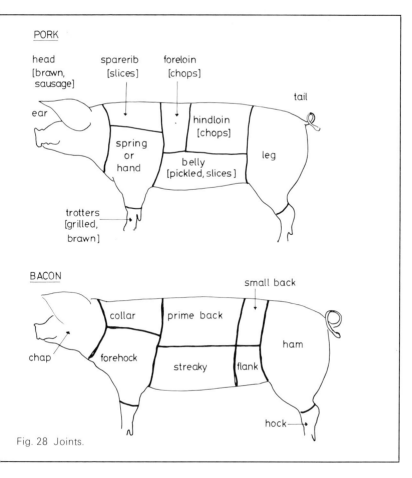

PORK

head
[brawn,
sausage]

sparerib
[slices]

foreloin
[chops]

tail

ear

hindloin
[chops]

spring
or
hand

belly
[pickled, slices]

leg

trotters
[grilled,
brawn]

BACON

small back

collar

prime back

ham

chap

forehock

streaky

flank

hock

Fig. 28 Joints.

written instructions as to how you wish it to be
jointed. Some butchers will joint, bag and blast freeze
for you so all that has to be done is to label the packs
with the joint and the date before placing them in your
deep-freeze.

Home butchery. In the old days before refrigeration the
pig was slaughtered only when there was an 'r' in the
month. Pig meat quickly goes bad and is readily fly-
blown. By September the worst of the heat of summer
has gone.

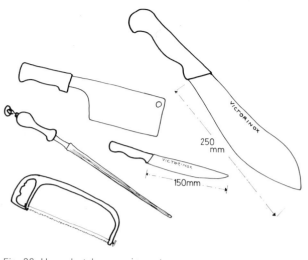

Fig. 29 Home butchery equipment.

We seem to have solved the butchery problem by bringing home the hung carcase and leaving it, skin side down, on a strong, old kitchen table in a cool fly-, cat- and dog-proof room to await the cutting. Our butcher friend arrives at eight o'clock in the morning and within a couple of hours the job is complete. He bones as much as is possible to make the meat more easily packed into the deep-freeze. Butchering is an art but you may feel confident to try it yourself having seen it done two or three times.

Home butchery kit :
1. A strong kitchen table. We have an Edwardian solid mahogany dining table which has stood up to the test of numerous cattle, pigs, sheep and goats being dismembered on it.
2. A chopping board. We made one from old-type orange-box ends. The boards were cut to equal lengths and then secured crossways three deep and this has proved to be a reasonably strong chopping board.

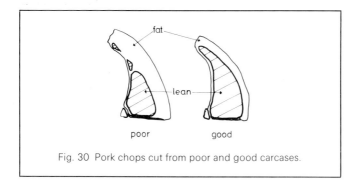

Fig. 30 Pork chops cut from poor and good carcases.

3. A meat cleaver. ⎫ Buy these from a butcher's sun-
4. Two knives.   ⎬ driesman as the domestic im-
5. A meat saw.   ⎭ itations are useless.
6. String.
7. Skewers.
8. Plastic bags of assorted sizes, labels, freezer tape.

The pluck

These pieces must be dealt with as soon as possible which is why they should be collected on the day of slaughter. The constituents of the pluck will vary, depending on the area in which you live. It may consist of only the heart, lungs, windpipe and liver (though in some areas even the liver is not included). Make sure though, that you get everything to which you are entitled which will also include the spleen, gullet and gut fat and possibly some trimmings. There will also be the mesentery.

Pluck recipes

Faggots
    400 g pig's fry (liver, heart and melts (spleen))
    large chopped onion
    75 g breadcrumbs
    salt and black pepper
    1 caul (mesentery)

Chop onion and sweat in pan till soft. Moisten bread-

63

crumbs in a little water, squeeze out moisture. Mince all the pig's fry and cook gently for 10 minutes. Add breadcrumbs, onion and seasoning. Soak the caul in warm water till pliable and cut in 120-mm-square pieces. Wrap the caul around the mixture making little parcels. Bake at 150°C (300°F), mark 5, till brown and sizzling.

Liver. To appreciate this at its best eat some of it fried as soon as you get it home. Cut through the lobes in slices with a sharp knife. The gall bladder will have been removed at the slaughterhouse.

Liver and pork pâté
The delight of liver pâté is that it never turns out the same twice.

    200 g pig's liver
    200 g belly of pork
    200 g sausage meat
    1 beaten egg
    Seasoning
    2 tablespoons of brandy if possible (sherry will do)
    2 tablespoons rolled oats
    enough streaky rashers to line the tin

Mince together at least three times all ingredients except egg and bacon. Mix in egg and brandy and place in bacon-lined tin. Place tin in baking dish half full of water. Bake at about 150°C (300°F), mark 5, until 1) mix comes away from sides; 2) there is fat floating about on top; 3) a warm skewer comes out clean.

I like to cover with a piece of foil and then press with at least a kilogram weight till cold. The pâté improves with keeping and will last at least a week if kept in a fridge. It should be slightly pink in the middle when sliced.

Using everything but the squeak

Fat. Any fat is best cut in small pieces or minced. This can then either be put in an old stone jar in a cool oven to render, or placed in a saucepan with a little water and simmered. The melted fat is then poured off into bowls and left to set. The result is *superb* lard. The same method is used for any surplus fat on the carcase (e.g. fat cut off the chops if they are too fat for your taste). This lard, wrapped in greaseproof paper, keeps well in a refrigerator.

Tail. This can be simmered gently in a little water till the large bones are soft enough to be easily pierced with a fork. It is delicious with English mustard and new potatoes.

Head. The simplest way to utilise this item is to make it into brawn. The head will have been riven in two at the slaughterhouse. First remove the eyes. A good-sized fish kettle will take the two head halves. Wash and half cover with water and bring to the boil, skim and bring to the boil again. Add some peppercorns, some lemon peel and a couple of blades of mace. Simmer till tender. (I put it in the simmering oven of the Aga cooker which is ideal as it cooks really gently.) When it is cooked, cool until you can bear your hand in the liquid. Remove all flesh and skin from the head *carefully* including tongue, mouthpieces, etc and dice. (I find some people don't like the ears and so they and the nostrils are consigned to the dogs but if included in the brawn they give texture.) The cheek may be a little fat so that can also be excluded where necessary. Reduce the liquid after straining until it is a quarter of the volume. Add salt, pepper, nutmeg to the meat and put in moulds. Top up with the liquid and cool. The aim is not to boil the head too vigorously or the liquid will be cloudy and the meat stringy.

Alternatively the head can be used for sausage meat by cutting off all available and accessible meat and boiling the remains of the head for brawn.

Ears. These should be soaked in salt water for 3 to 4 hours. Boil in a half litre (1 pint) of water and skim off the grey scum. Add carrot, onions, herbs and simmer till tender but not falling to pieces—about 2 hours. Cool and then slice into 10-mm strips, coat in batter and fry. This is crunchy and delicious on a cold day— but don't tell anyone what it is.

Trotters. This is a rich dish which I learnt from an elderly countryman. Simmer gently till a fork goes into the thick bone (this is a dish which you leave on the stove all day to simmer and which you eat when you are hungry). Cool a little and then brush with dry mustard and breadcrumbs and grill till crisp and sizzling. Eat using your fingers and wear a towel around your neck.

Raised pork pies. I have not been successful making these. They turned out to be heavy and extremely filling. However, there are excellent recipes in most cookery books.

Sausages. The bones can be scraped once more after the butchering and these little bits of meat saved for sausages. The thinner end of the belly piece can also be utilised. There will inevitably be odd pieces of lean trimmed off the joints which are ideal for the sausage bowl. If the head is not used for brawn this can be boned out and used, including the tongue.

One possible method is to cut all the bits into approximately 20-mm-square pieces. These can then be minced but be sure to include a certain amount of fat otherwise the sausages will be *very* solid. Mince a second time and then place in a large washing-up bowl. The following is our usual recipe, arrived at by trial and error—needless to say, it never tastes the same twice!

3 kg pieces
15 g black pepper freshly milled
up to 50 g salt
half a nutmeg, grated
a good pinch of mace
15 g sage (if liked)

The secret of good sausages is to buy the spices *freshly* the day before. Try to find a reliable grocer or delicatessen shop where there is a quick turnover to ensure that the spice is really fresh.

Mix very thoroughly by hand and cook a small portion in the frying pan to see if the seasoning is to your liking. We then roll small lumps of the sausage meat in slightly dampened hands (so that it does not stick), press into discs 80 mm across by 10 mm thick. These are then laid on cellophane sheets and frozen separately before being thrown together into a large bag, sealed and labelled with the date stamped on.

Such sausage meat is best eaten within three months. It is possible to beg some skins from a local butcher or buy either plastic or real ones (made from intestine) from a butcher's sundriesman.

The actual pork is recommended to be kept in the deep-freeze for not longer than six months but the oldest pork we have eaten was two years. Perhaps it is best not to keep it too long as the fat is said to go rancid.

Bacon

If there is a local butcher who cures and smokes, then this is the lazy man's way out. The sides of pork are delivered to him and two weeks later the joints of cured and smoked bacon are collected. This is suitable for summer-killed pigs and would be a mild cure. Freeze the bacon in joints (do not slice before freezing as it will go off more quickly). Bag in two thicknesses of plastic to prevent the bacon tainting the rest of the freezer contents, label and date. If this easy method is employed, it is worth doing a little surgery before you deliver the sides:

1. Take off the head if you wish to make it into sausages or brawn.
2. Pull out the flare. This is the layer of fat running along the inside of the ribs and makes the very best lard.
3. Trim off the pieces of meat proud from the ribs and which held the gut in place.
4. Run a finger along under the backbone and pull out the undercut (or tenderloin). It will need cutting down by the back leg.
5. Cut off the trotters if you like them grilled.

If the pig has been killed in the winter it may be worth curing and salting at home. We have found that the easiest method is to joint the side and cure the pieces for different lengths of time depending on the thickness. If the bacon is to be frozen it will need only a mild cure and all the pieces can be cured for the same period.

Suffolk cure. We found the ingredients for this cure expensive but the result is very subtle, if a little sweet.

You will need a large vessel; a plastic dustbin will do but it will only take one side of the pig.

For the pickle:
18 litres water
9 kg black treacle
2 blocks salt

50 g saltpetre (obtainable from some chemists)
50 g black pepper
50 g juniper berries
half teacup vinegar

Simmer this mixture for half an hour and cool.

Joint the pig as you require. Rub meat *well* with dry salt and leave in an old earthenware sink. You may even find an original slate tank which is the correct vessel. Rub with salt daily for three days then drain and wash out the vessel. Pack meat in dustbin (not too compactly as you want the pickling solution to get to the meat). Pour the cold pickle over the meat. Turn the meat daily.

I make a point of doing the turning first thing in the morning so that I don't forget. One ham that I turned infrequently was distinctly odd-tasting! The joints, all but the hams, will be ready in three weeks and the hams in about four weeks. If the hams are very large (say 10 kg or so) they will need about six weeks in the pickle and it may also be necessary to let the pickle infiltrate into the centre of the joint more effectively. In this case make an incision near the knuckle before the curing begins and rub in the cure thoroughly for the first week. In warmish weather such as we sometimes get in October watch out for a yellow mould. If this appears I immediately rub in more neat salt and it usually disappears.

When the cure is complete take out the bacon and thoroughly wipe it dry and hang in a cool, dark, dry place—our back hall is ideal. After three days the flitches can be sewn into old sheets to keep out moths and flies and hung up to mature. They can be eaten within a few weeks but will improve with age. Before eating the bacon will need soaking for about twelve hours prior to boiling.

I was given a particularly good recipe for a ham, which is as follows:

200 g moist brown sugar
200 g bay salt (I have not been able to procure this, but I gather a coarse salt will do)
25 g saltpetre
1 litre wine vinegar

As mentioned above make an incision beside the knuckle then rub the meat well with extra dry salt, the flesh and the skin being covered thoroughly. Leave for three days and then wipe dry. Mix the sugar, salt and saltpetre and rub thoroughly all over. Leave for three more days in a large, deep, plastic washing-up bowl. Pour the wine vinegar over and turn the ham daily for a month; take out and carefully dry, then follow with smoking. The cured ham is very good even without smoking but in either case it will need to mature for a month or so after treatment is completed.

It is always worth making a note of the weight of the ham, the exact cure and the length of time soaked so that this can be used to modify the procedures with subsequent cures.

If you want to smoke bacon this is done as soon as the joints are dry.

Smoking. Originally smokehouses were buildings with a chimney at the top and a roof about 2.5 metres from the floor with hooks in it. The *oak* sawdust is put on the ground and ignited so that it smokes and does not flame up with the door of the house closed. A light smoking for bacon to be stored in the deep-freeze will take about twelve hours, but smoked bacon which is to be stored hung needs forty-eight hours or so. A friend of ours smokes his bacon in the chimney of his prefab as he has a wood-burning stove—he climbs on to the roof to hang the meat at the top of the chimney. If you are lucky enough to have a large chimney there may still be hooks there for hanging fish and meat but it must hang at least 2 metres from the source of the smoke.

Health in the Pig Sty

A healthy, happy pig is likely to be both profitable and flavoursome. It is worth spending some time quietly watching and listening to your pigs at any odd moment you have during the day. You will then recognise what is normal. Some pigs are most *talkative*—always grunting, grumbling, snorting or squealing. Others are mostly silent except when they hear the pig bucket or if they wish to register their extreme disapproval. Any departure from their normal voice is to be noted with suspicion. Silence in a normally vociferous animal can be the first sign that all is not well.

The head

A healthy pig has an alert appearance. His *eye*, though small compared with that of some other animals, is round and bright with no obvious signs of stickiness around the lids; the mucous membrane inside the lower eyelid should be salmon pink. His *mouth* is clean and often held a little open when interested. Pigs investigate with their mouths like human babies. Anything strange is often explored and possibly nibbled or bitten. The *snout* should be moist, clean and shining; it is highly mobile as well as being extremely strong.

The ears

These are held in different attitudes according to the

breed. The outer skin should look healthy, be shining and covered in small, coarse hairs. The inside of the ear should be obviously gleaming and free from excessive grease, dirt, encrustations of scabs or loose, dead skin. Lower down in the ear there are a few coarse hairs which help prevent the entry of foreign bodies. The healthy pig's ears are warm; cold, clammy or burning-hot ears will show that all is not well.

The body

All pigs are covered with coarse hairs to a greater or lesser extent depending on the breed and whether they are kept indoors or outdoors; an ill-fed runt may develop a coarse, hairy coat as a protection. The *skin* in all pigs should be shiny and free from loose, dead skin, scabbiness or wrinkles. The *tail* is generally curled (though some healthy pigs hang them straight down intermittently when feeding) and is a fair guide to the animal's general health. Often a runt will arrive with a hanging tail. Within a week of peace and quiet, possibly improved feeding and generally optimum conditions, its tail will assume the jaunty curl of a healthy pig.

Dung

The smell of the healthy pig's dung is not unpleasant. It is passed in the form of firmish, cylindrical, fairly large pellets, the colour being affected to a certain degree by the food the animal is given. Animals being fed a proprietary ration containing copper can pass blue-grey dung. This may also be noticed in pigs kept intensively and having access to acorns or wood ash. Otherwise the outside of the pellets should be brown and have a slightly fibrous look. Mucilaginous or bloody dung is not normal and your vet is best called; it can be caused by swine dysentery. However, loose droppings may be caused purely by some mechanical upset, a change of diet or too much greenstuff; but if the condition changes from sloppiness to liquid call the vet. The healthy pig generally dungs in the lowest corner (if any), usually sited as far away from feeding and sleeping areas as possible. Given the chance, pigs are extremely fastidious but in very hot weather they may wallow in dung and urine in an attempt to keep cool.

The *smell* of both urine and dung should not be offensive or strong. Experience is clearly vital here, but an obviously unpleasant aroma in the dunging area will put the stockman on his guard.

Respiration

The normal rate should be about 20 to 30 per minute and can be easily counted while the animal is in repose (a respiratory movement being a complete rise and fall of the flanks and chest). This will not be obviously laboured in the healthy pig; the younger the animal the faster the respiration. Warm conditions will also increase the rate. Our tame, backyard pigs will not be so likely to show differences in respiration due to alarm caused by handling or the presence of strangers.

Temperature

This can be taken by greasing the bulb of a clinical thermometer and inserting it gently into the rectum. It should normally read about 38°C (101.5°F). However it varies with the external temperature and the conditions under which the animal is kept. Under certain circumstances 39°C (103°F) can be considered normal. Do not put too much emphasis on the animal's rectal temperature as it is so variable.

Younger animals usually have a slightly higher temperature than the older ones. The temperature of a young pig after exercise normally rises a little. I have never used a thermometer on a pig as I feel I *should* know by feeling the animal's shoulder and its ears (and also by its general attitude) if it has a temperature. Any departure from the norm is best reported to the vet. An animal showing no symptoms apart from a raised temperature *can be dead* by the morning.

Attitude

Pigs are active, violent creatures, food being consumed with great avidity; exercise is taken boisterously, barking the while with delight. Rest is taken suddenly—the nest being put to rights before they lie flat out, dropping off to sleep apparently instantaneously (until you see one eye surreptitiously peeping through the straw). However, sleep can be alarmingly deep; an apparently dead animal can leap to life in a moment!

Suspect any animal which does not rush to the food bowl. Inspect the dung, feel his ears and look at his respiration. Check his drinking water—dirty water will lead to extreme thirst and consequent failure to eat. During the summer a couple of rearers will need at least one bucket of fresh water at each feed, and I like to renew it at mid-day as well.

Overfeeding

Newly acquired pigs are best under- rather than over-fed ('there are more pigs killed by overfeeding than underfeeding' . . . traditional saying). The stress of moving, strange surroundings and a possible change of feed may cause the animals to scour. They need quiet surroundings with plenty of litter and clean water. Many pig keepers give only one feed on every seventh day to rest the gut of older, fattening stock. This does not mean that you do not have to keep an eye on the stock for this period. However, if this is tried see they have plenty of water and adequate clean straw in which to nose around on this day.

Your veterinary surgeon

It is as well to cast around amongst the farming fraternity to find out where the good local veterinary surgeons are located before you embark on your piggy enterprise. It is no good leaving the situation till 11.30 one night when urgent professional attention is needed. Make a note of the telephone number and keep this in a *prominent* place near the telephone.

On calling the vet with any signs and symptoms you may have noticed, give him your name, telephone number and clear instructions how to find your home. Next, ensure adequate lighting is available if it is dark. Open your gate for him so that he does not have to waste time on his way to the pig shed. On his arrival don't overwhelm him with irrelevant detail—allow him to question you. Do follow the vet's instructions and complete any treatment meticulously. Offer him facilities to wash his boots and hands before leaving. Many vets will be only too pleased to discuss a problem and offer advice over the telephone.

Diseases

Diarrhoea. This will be readily observed in the dunging area as well as on the pig's back parts. It can be caused *mechanically* by a change in the type of food or it may be *infectious*. If it is caused by an infection you will obviously have a sick pig, lethargic and dull with little or no appetite. However, in the case of swine dysentery the animal still feeds and is relatively lively but it will be heavily soiled down its back legs with a mixture of dung, blood and mucus.

Newly born pigs with neonatal scours will pass watery faeces and show sore back legs. They will

75

rapidly lose weight and will be obviously sick. Call the vet promptly.

There are several virus conditions which will cause scouring in pigs of all ages which necessitate veterinary investigation.

It cannot be emphasised too strongly that in *all cases* of diarrhoea pigs must have constant access to clean, fresh water to prevent dehydration. If by any chance they do run out of water they will drink urine or their sloppy dung and transmit the infection.

Swine erysipelas (also known as diamond disease). This is recognisable when a normally active pig *suddenly* becomes dull and does not feed. There will be raised red swellings (6 to 40 mm) on its body and its temperature will rise drastically. Call the vet who will treat the animal.

Erysipelas is caused by a soil-borne organism which is *not* highly infectious and it may only affect one pig in a group. However, it can leave the animal with a weak heart and arthritis which makes it inadvisable to keep any affected animals as breeding stock.

Pneumonia. This is essentially a disease of overcrowding and is unlikely to cause problems in the backyard piggery. In the long term it may cause the animals to fatten more slowly. Should it arise, the symptoms are increased respiratory rate, mild coughing, dullness and lack of appetite. A course of antibiotics from the vet, either injected or administered in the drinking water, may alleviate the situation in conjunction with well-ventilated housing.

Notifiable diseases
The law makes it obligatory for owners of pigs to keep a record of all movements on and off the premises (see

page 88 for movements record). This is to enable the police and the animal health division of ADAS to take control in the event of your vet diagnosing the following four diseases:

Anthrax. This is now a very rare disease, and one which can affect man. If you suddenly find a dead pig, inform the local divisional veterinary office and they will send a veterinary officer. Further information about this disease is contained in HMSO Advisory Leaflet No. 74.

Swine fever. In 1966 this disease was eradicated from the United Kingdom but in 1971 there was a small outbreak. It is *highly* infectious.

Foot and mouth disease. This disease affects all cloven-hoofed animals. Possible symptoms are lameness, blisters on claws, snout and possibly on the teats, excessive salivation and temperatures up to 41°C (106°F).

If foot and mouth disease breaks out locally, telephone your divisional veterinary office where you will be given instructions as to what precautions to take.

Swine vesicular disease (SVD). This disease is peculiar to pigs. However, as the symptoms are only distinguishable from foot and mouth disease by laboratory investigation it must not go unchecked as it could spread rapidly. It is transmitted by *inadequately treated swill.*

External parasites
Lice. These black creatures up to 7 mm across are often seen on pigs even when in the best of health. They cause more distress to the owners than to the

pigs. However, the presence of lice may draw your attention to other parasitic problems.

Cooper's or ICI louse powder rubbed into the back, behind and in the ears and also inside the thighs, repeated after a fortnight to catch the hatched eggs, will help to keep the infestation down.

Preventive action. Thoroughly scrub all buildings between batches and burn litter from heavily infested stock.

Mange. This is not so pleasant, as humans can catch it, but it is relatively easy to eradicate with proprietary louse and mange parasiticide (wash) from the vet or agricultural chemist. This parasite is not visible to the naked eye. It burrows into the pores of the skin and causes intense irritation resulting in the animal rubbing with consequential unthriftiness. Grease on the walls up to pig-shoulder height indicates rubbing and should arouse your suspicions.

Small pigs suffering from mange can be ducked head first in the parasiticide wash for three seconds, taking care not to drown them! When bringing new stock on to your premises (especially if the insides of their ears are at all black and waxy) ladle the wash into each ear with a tablespoon.

Internal parasites

Some pigs carry worms. Any unthrifty animals, especially those bought from large pig units which may have a worm problem, can be treated with a broad-spectrum vermifuge from the vet. Some worms are too small to be seen with the naked eye, so their presence may go unsuspected.

Round worms. These are up to 30 cm long. The pig eats material containing the worm eggs, the larvae are coughed up and reswallowed, eventually maturing in the intestine. They are usually passed out in the dung but *may* be vomited up in a severe infestation. Pigs are only likely to pick up round worms if they or the sows have had access to pasture. Good hygiene will prevent reinfestation by preventing the passage of eggs from dung to mouth.

Poisons

Lead. Where pigs are kept on older premises they may gain access to timber treated with lead paint. The animal will only need a flake or two off an old door. It may be found with its head turned back over its neck prior to convulsions. Four to six beaten eggs can be administered as a drench while professional aid is summoned.

Salt. This can occur in pigs fed household swill. It may leave the animals excessively thirsty and they can die if deprived of water. On a normal diet pigs without access to adequate water can show the nervous symptoms associated with salt poisoning. These are lack of co-ordination, staggering and fits.

Arsenic. Arsenic in very small quantities is used in the treatment of swine dysentery. Over-medication or shortage of water can lead to poisoning, the symptom being increasing lack of co-ordination.

Yew. Death is sudden and there is no antidote.

Laburnum. The leaves will cause acute dysentery (not the infectious variety). Call the vet.

Acorns. The shells of acorns contain tannic acid which will cause extreme constipation. Most free-range stock will naturally dehusk the acorn before eating it. Liquid paraffin may relieve those who fail to do this.

Bracken. Pigs allowed free range may eat both rhizome (root) and frond. It is almost invariably fatal, except perhaps in the older native breeds, e.g. Gloucester Old Spot. The symptom of intractable scouring may be alleviated by a high cereal diet.

Potato. Potatoes allowed to become green through exposure to light are poisonous as are the haulm and shoots. Symptoms of poisoning are extreme drowsiness and low body temperature. Large quantities of sweet, strong, warm tea can be administered as a general stimulant and first aid treatment while the vet is being called.

Medicine chest
Complete vermifuge from vet
Mange wash
Paint marking stick
Stockholm tar for cuts
Tablespoon
Restraining noose
Small copper nose rings ⎫
Bull rings   ⎬ for outdoor pigs
Ring pliers   ⎭

8 Bits and Pieces

Litter
The litter most commonly used with pigs is straw. It is comparatively cheap, easily obtainable and, when combined with dung and urine, makes an excellent garden manure after composting. Wheat straw is often the cheapest but is not so absorbent as barley; it may be sharp and scratchy. Barley straw is more expensive as the spring-sown varieties are often used

for cattle fodder. Winter-sown barley straw may be cheaper as it is less palatable to cattle but still provides a comfortable and absorbent bedding. Oat straw is not particularly absorbent but is used for cattle fodder and is therefore a little more expensive than wheat straw.

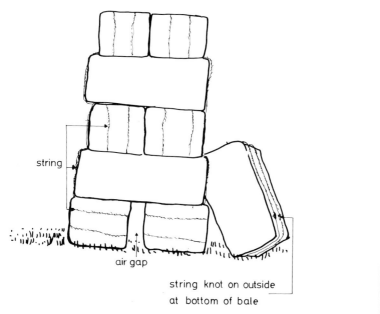

string

air gap

string knot on outside
at bottom of bale

Fig. 31 Stacking straw bales. This is reasonably weatherproof for a day or two.

The cheapest way to obtain straw is to contact a farmer some time before harvest and arrange to buy it ready-baled on the field. He will usually expect you to cart it or he may charge a little more and deliver it for you. If you collect do try to clear the straw as soon as possible, as many farmers like to cultivate the fields as soon after harvest as they can. We try to stand the straw in stacks of ten bales immediately after baling prior to carting it home the next day. Fifty bales should provide ample bedding for two pairs of pigs for one year. Store it under cover if at all possible.

Fig. 32 Composting pig manure.

Mucking out

The quickest and most comfortable method for all concerned when keeping only a few pigs is to clean out the dunging area daily. Pigs kept indoors will generally use the furthest point from the sleeping area. A good, strong shovel is needed to scrape up this material and this will take but a couple of minutes. If this is done twice daily after feeding the pen will keep clean and sweet. It is a good plan to collect a little dung and place in the corner you wish used *before* the pigs are put in and usually they will continue to use this area. They will inevitably dung on the journey home so this material can be used for training.

The manure heap

This is best sited as near to both vegetable patch and sty as possible. Mark an area 2 m by 1 m and try to build the heap with vertical sides. An old piece of corrugated iron or plastic fertiliser bag placed on top will prevent rain leaching out the goodness and will also keep in the heat which helps compost the material quickly.

Fig. 33 Cleaning-out tools.

Tools

Besides the strong shovel, a wheelbarrow (strong galvanised metal is lighter than a wooden one), a nylon-bristled yard brush, a hand scrubbing brush, a round-pronged 4-tined fork, a hay fork and a bucket will be needed for the pig unit. It is worth buying good-quality tools and keeping them cleaned and greased where possible. Manure is *very* corrosive.

Clothes

Pig dung has a remarkably persistent aroma which penetrates and clings to most clothing. An old boiler suit for use when working with the pigs and kept hanging in the meal store will prove an ideal covering. Rubber gloves will prevent the cheese soufflé from tasting of pig. A hat is a useful extra as straw is remarkably dusty. Aim to brush off wellington boots in a trough kept especially for this purpose. It may prove a valuable disease inhibitor if Jeyes' fluid or Dettol is added to the water. Visitors can then be asked to dip their feet on arrival and departure.

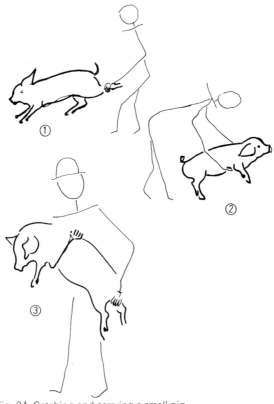

Fig. 34 Catching and carrying a small pig.

Handling pigs

Pigs are intelligent creatures and learn incredibly fast—especially bad habits! Watch an expert pig handler catching a small pig. He stalks it quietly (no chasing), grasps it by a back leg (or both), then holds it behind the shoulder with both hands and lifts it up quickly before it can get a purchase on the ground. The pig soon learns that struggling is ineffective. However it will also very quickly learn to evade a maladroit pursuer.

Fig. 35 Moving pigs. Let them move slowly to a new place.

Within a week or two of weaning, the pig will have grown too heavy and strong to be lifted. If the pig's natural instinct to make for a gap is exploited, the simplest way to move it will be to allow it but one way to go. This is achieved by holding a solid board at either side of its head which will encourage the animal to move forward. Before long the second board holder can be dispensed with and the first driver can replace the second board with a wooden bat about 1 metre long. Obviously it is useless to expect a pig to conform

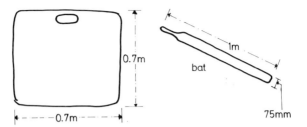

Fig. 36 Bat and board for guiding pigs. The bat is *not* to be used for hitting the animals.

the first time and a combination of both patience and firmness will be needed. This method will be ineffective with six-week-old pigs; their first aim in life is to run anywhere at high speed, kicking and squealing.

It is a waste of time attempting to drive a pig with a group of people—it will turn and charge, making for any gap between the drivers and is quite capable of hurtling through the legs of any one of them.

Ringing pigs

If the pasture is not to be thoroughly ploughed by the pigs within days of them being put out to graze, some

Fig. 37 Self-piercing bullring for sow. The ring is inserted, then turned around in the nose. A small screw holds the two ends together.

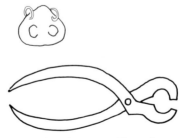

Fig. 38 Two copper rings for rearers. These rings are inserted with ringing pliers.

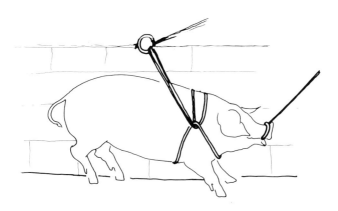
Fig. 39 Restraining a pig for ringing. It will pull backwards.

form of restraint will have to be used. The most effective is ringing the nose. The simplest way is to do this when the pigs are first weaned as they will be easier to hold. They are sure to lose a ring sometime so it is worth putting in two while you are doing the job. One person will be needed to hold the pig by its front legs while the nose is held in position with a noose. Two small copper rings can then be inserted into the thick rim of the snout, one on either side. These will generally last the life of a fattening pig. A breeding sow will need a bull ring inserted into the nostrils.

Transporting weaner pigs
The easiest way to transport weaners is to construct a solid-sided crate with a floor-hinged door at either end which can double as a ramp. The crate is best lined with plastic fertiliser bags covered with a little soil (to absorb any urine) and topped off with straw for comfort. The crate can be made so as to fit your own transport, but must be high enough for the pig to stand up but not wide enough for it to be able to turn around. The framework of the crate will need to be on the outside so that the animal is presented with

87

smooth surfaces. A couple of vigorous weaners can soon shatter an ineffectively constructed crate.

9 Pigs and the Law

Pigs can fall prey to certain highly infectious diseases and in order to maintain some control the Ministry of Agriculture, Fisheries and Food (MAFF) has devised a system of restricting all pig movements by the issue of movement permits and licences.

Everyone owning pigs, cattle, sheep or goats must make a record of all movements on or off their premises within thirty-six hours after the movement of the animal. This record must be made in ink or indelible pencil in a book which must be made available to any inspector on behalf of the Divisional Veterinary Investigation (DVI) Department of the Agricultural Development and Advisory Service (ADAS).

For pigs in particular, there is the Movement and Sale of Pigs Order 1975 which restricts the movement of animals without a licence (copies obtainable from the local authority or the local Divisional Veterinary Office). Further information regarding these restrictions, which *must be strictly adhered to* if the spread of disease is to be controlled, can be obtained from your local DVI office who will send the appropriate literature and forms.

There are certain diseases—anthrax, swine fever, foot and mouth and swine vesicular disease—which come under the Notifiable Diseases Order which states that any suspected case of any of these diseases must be reported at once to the vet and to the DVI office who will then indicate what immediate proceedings are to be taken.

As a precaution against the transmission of disease by the feeding of swill (which has either animal content or has been in contact with animal wastes) the authorities have devised the Diseases of Animals (Waste Food) Order. Copies of the order and the regulations concerning the feeding of swill may be obtained from the DVI office.

All premises which feed animal waste or anything that has been in contact with animal waste *must be licensed*. The processing equipment must be housed in specially constructed buildings with completely separate, animal- and bird-proof reception and discharge areas. The waste must be *boiled* for at least one hour and this receptacle must be placed so that access can be gained to it from both discharge and reception areas. The running of these premises comes under stringent regulations and inspections can occur monthly at any unspecified time.

Waste with no animal content or that which has not been in contact with meat of any kind is not covered by the order—e.g. greengrocer's and baker's waste.

Appendix I

Further Reading

Her Majesty's Stationery Office Bulletins:
    Housing the Pig No. 160
    Diseases of Pigs No. 171
    Pig Husbandry and Management No. 193
    British Poisonous Plants No. 161
    Electric Fencing No. 147

HMSO Advisory Leaflets:
    Pig Feeding No. 104
    Management of Young Pigs No. 508
    Swine Erysipelas No. 17
    Anthrax No. 74
    Swine Fever No. 83
    Transmissible Gastroenteritis TGE No. 573

Books:
    The Pig Farmer's Veterinary Handbook by Norman Barron, Farming Press
    Production and Marketing of Pigs by H. R. Davidson, Longmans
    Pig Management and Production by Derek H. Goodwin, Hutchinson
    Comfrey, Past, Present and Future by Lawrence D. Hills, Faber
    Build Your Own Farm Buildings by Frank Henderson, Farming Press
    Herbal Handbook for Farm and Stable by Juliette de Bairacli Levy, Faber
    The Complete Book of Self-Sufficiency by John Seymour, Faber
    Feeding of Livestock by S. J. Watson, Nelson
    Backyard Pig Book by Ann Williams, Prism Press
    Home Smoking and Curing by Keith Erlandson, Barrie & Jenkins
    Keeping Livestock Healthy by N. Bruce Haynes, DVM
    'TV Vet' Book for Pigfarmers, The Farming Press
    Pigkeeper's Guide by Michelmore, David & Charles

Small Scale Pig Raising by Dirk van Loon, Gardenway
    Publishers (USA)
The Book of the Pig by Susan Hulme, Saiga
Outdoor Pig Production by Keith Thornton,
    The Farming Press

Periodicals:
    Pig Farmer
    Practical Self Sufficiency, bimonthly
    Smallholder, monthly

Homeopathic Society quarterly newsletter, New Parc,
    Llanrhidian, Gower, Glamorgan, SA3 1AH.

Appendix II

Useful Addresses

National Pig Breeders Association,
7 Rickmansworth Road, Watford, Herts. WD1 7HE

Artificial Insemination,
MLC Pig Breeding Centre, Leeds Road, Thorpe Willoughby, Selby,
Yorkshire

Rare Breeds Survival Trust,
4th Street, N.A.C., Stoneleigh, Warks. CV8 2IG

Suppliers of equipment:

Small Scale Supplies,
Widdington, Saffron Walden, Essex CB11 3SP

Self Sufficiency & Smallholding Supplies,
Priory Road, Wells, Somerset

Weigh Band, Alfred Cox,
Edward Road, Coulsdon, Surrey

Dalton's,
Nettlebed, Oxfordshire

Lincolnshire Smallholders Supplies Ltd.,
Willow Farm, Thorpe Fendykes, Wainfleet, Lincs.

Index

94